This book belongs to

....

IT IS
TOP SECRET,
SO
KEEP OUT!
YES, THAT MEANS YOU...

Published 2013. Century Books Ltd.
Unit 1, Upside Station Building Solsbro Road,
Torquay, Devon, UK, TQ26FD

books@centurybooksltd.co.uk

Contents

HELLO KITTY

What are your favourite things in life?

Cheerful and kind, Kitty is a cute little cat whose motto is 'you can never have too many friends.' She is very popular and loves to hang out with her besties Tracy, Fifi and Dear Daniel. Kitty is multi talented and has loads of hobbies from baking scrummy cookies to painting, playing the piano, origami and collecting ribbons.

I LOVE HELLO KITTY

Factfile

NAME: KITTY WHITE
BIRTHDAY: 1 NOVEMBER
LIVES: LONDON, ENGLAND
LIKES: HER PERSIAN PET, CHARMMY KITTY AND HER FLUFFY HAMSTER, SUGAR
FAVE THING: HER MUM'S HOMEMADE APPLE PIE

Cute-o-meter!

cute **really cute** **super cute**

DRAW AN ARROW ON THE CUTE-O-METER TO SHOW HOW CUTE YOU THINK KITTY IS.

The thing I like most about Kitty is: ....

If I ever met Kitty I would...

Listen to some tunes with her ( )   Ask her for her cookie recipe ( )   Get her to teach me origami ( )

HOW TO DRAW KITTY

1. DRAW A SIDEWAYS OVAL, FOR KITTY'S HEAD WITH A SQUARE WITH ROUND EDGES UNDERNEATH IT, FOR HER BODY.

2. ADD ROUNDED-CORNER TRIANGLES TO THE OVAL FOR KITTY'S EARS AND A CIRCLE AND TWO ROUNDED-CORNER TRIANGLES TO CREATE HER BOW.

3. NEXT, ADD HER EYES, NOSE AND THREE WHISKERS ON EITHER SIDE OF HER HEAD.

4. THEN ADD TWO ARMS TO THE SIDE OF HER BODY AND DRAW IN HER LEGS AND HER CLOTHES. TO FINISH, COLOUR HER IN.

7

Kitty's Doodle Time

Grab your pencil and show off your artistic
skills with oodles of doodles…

**What do you think Kitty
is daydreaming about?
Doodle in the dream
bubble below.**

**Doodle some
new patterns
on Kittys
bows.**

Fancy yourself as a jewellery designer?
Turn these doodles into some fab jewels for Kitty.

Use the dotted lines to
finish kitty's dress and
bow then create
a cute pattern.

9

Family Fun

Being part of a family is brilliant! Even if your parents, sisters and brothers can drive your loopy at times it's great having people you can always count on and who'll love you forever.

Fill in your family tree and draw a picture or stick a photo in the photo frames, to show who's who in your family.

Did you know?
Keroppi admires his dad, who is a doctor and helps cure sick frogs. He thinks his mum's job as a chef is cool too, because she makes the most delicious rice balls ever – his fave food!

Who is the cuddliest in your family?: ....

Who has the loudest laugh?: ....

Who has the worst habit?: ....

Who is the most annoying?: ....

Who is the coolest?: ....

Did you know?
Kitty has a cute twin sister called Mimi. You can always tell them apart as Kitty wears her ribbon on her left ear and Mimi wears hers on her right.

Who is the messiest?: ....

Who is the funniest?: ....

Who talks the most?: ....

Which TV show is your family most like?: ....

Who do you look like in your family? ....

What do your parents do? ....

Who teaches you cool things in your family? ....

Did you know?
My Melody loves spending time with her family and learning things from them – like how to make delicious cakes and cookies. Who teaches you cool things in your family?

Wordplay

Can you find the Sanrio gang in the puzzle?
Their names can be found horizontally, vertically and
diagonally, both forwards and backwards.

PANDAPPLE   KEROPPI

                    BADTZ-MARU

CHOCOCAT   HELLO KITTY

                    PIPPO

MONKICHI

                              DEAR DANIEL

            CINNAMOROLL

KUROMI   LANDRY

    SPOTTIE DOTTIE   TUXEDOSAM

                LITTLE TWIN STARS

                    POCHACCO

                    PEKKLE

                                **One of them
                                is missing,
                                can you work
                                out who?**

        MY MELODY

        PURIN

L	T	L	E	D	Y	L	M	M	N	W	C	Y	S	P
N	I	Z	E	R	H	Y	X	E	K	I	I	T	P	U
I	C	T	D	I	M	A	N	P	N	T	M	T	O	R
P	P	N	T	L	N	U	C	N	N	E	O	I	T	I
P	A	P	L	L	O	A	A	O	L	I	R	K	T	N
L	I	O	O	J	E	M	D	P	C	A	U	O	I	M
B	D	P	J	R	O	T	P	R	X	A	K	L	E	O
Y	R	F	P	R	E	A	W	R	A	A	X	L	D	N
T	E	M	O	O	D	K	J	I	L	E	G	E	O	K
Z	D	L	K	N	S	V	X	I	N	M	D	H	T	I
I	L	L	A	P	E	K	K	L	E	S	G	L	T	C
N	X	P	Y	J	Y	J	O	Y	G	L	T	K	I	H
T	U	X	E	D	O	S	A	M	F	G	K	A	E	I
U	R	A	M	Z	T	D	A	B	F	B	C	C	R	N
O	C	C	A	H	C	O	P	Z	Y	T	F	J	R	S

Answers on page 94

13

Fave Things

What are your favourite things in life?

Fave friend:...

Fave colour: ....

Fave family member: ....

Fave song: ....

Fave film: ....

Fave accessory: ....

Fave tv show: ....

Fave outfit: ....

Fave chocolate bar: ....

Fave shop: ....

Fave animal:...

Fave sport: ....

Fave food: ....

Fave drink: ....

Fave shoes: ....

Fave time of the year: ....

Fave day of the week: ....

14

Top 10 fave Sanrio characters:

1. ....   6. ....
2. ....   7. ....
3. ....   8. ....
4. ....   9. ....
5. ....   10. ....

How well do you know your Sanrio characters?
Tick the box to show what their fave things are.

HELLO KITTY

MARTIAL ARTS ♡

DANCING ♡

BAKING COOKIES ♡

KEROPPI

BIRD WATCHING ◯

SWIMMING IN DONUT POND ◯

READING COMICS ◯

Badtz-Maru

EXTREME SPORTS AND KICKING BUTT ◯

READING POETRY ◯

WATCHING SOPPY FILMS ◯

Kuromi

DOING HOMEWORK ★

GETTING UP TO NO GOOD ★

READING ROMANCE NOVELS ★

Answers on page 94

Secret Stuff

Everyone has something that makes them totally unique.
Kitty has her cute bow and Badtz-Maru has his mischief making,
so what makes **you**, totally **you**?

Hi there, I'm Kitty White, but my friends call me Kitty.

Name:...........................

Nickname: ....

Birthday: ....

Age: ....

Born in: ....

Star sign: ....

Live: ....

Best friend: ....

Pets: ....

Biggest achievement: ....

Proudest moment: ....

Most embarrassing moment: ....

Nicest thing about me: ....

Worst thing about me: ....

Eye colour:

brown ◯   green ◯

hazel ◯   blue ◯

Hair colour:

light brown ◯   dark brown ◯

red ◯   strawberry blonde ◯

blonde ◯   light blonde ◯   black ◯

Face shape:

round ◯   oval ◯   square ◯

long ◯   heart-shaped ◯

Stick a photo or draw of a picture of yourself here.

Best feature:

....

Worst feature:

....

The way you sign your name can reveal top-secret stuff about the type of person you are.

Sign here and see what your signature says about you.

Loopy writing

Relaxed

A loopy signature shows you are broad-minded and have a relaxed approach to life.

Illegible signature

what

If you can't read your name when you sign it, it means you like to keep some things private.

Size of your signature

A **big** and **bold** signature means you like to be noticed.
A small signature means you just want to fit in.

KEROPPI

Brave and bold, Keroppi is the most popular frog in Donut Pond. He loves going on adventures and playing games with his best mates Ganta and Kyorosuke. Nothing gets this cute and fun-loving little frog down for long, his cheerful and optimistic nature helps him bounce back in no time, ready for the next exciting adventure.

I LOVE KEROPPI

Kyorosuke   **Ganta**

Factfile

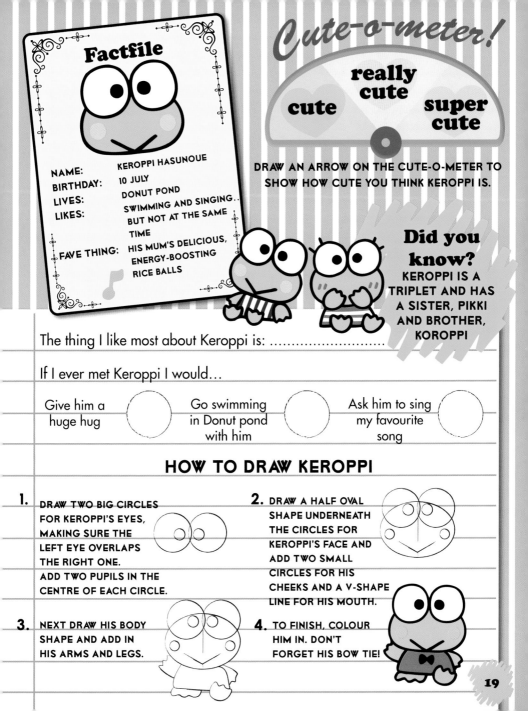

NAME: KEROPPI HASUNOUE
BIRTHDAY: 10 JULY
LIVES: DONUT POND
LIKES: SWIMMING AND SINGING... BUT NOT AT THE SAME TIME
FAVE THING: HIS MUM'S DELICIOUS, ENERGY-BOOSTING RICE BALLS

Cute-o-meter!

cute
really cute
super cute

DRAW AN ARROW ON THE CUTE-O-METER TO SHOW HOW CUTE YOU THINK KEROPPI IS.

Did you know?
KEROPPI IS A TRIPLET AND HAS A SISTER, PIKKI AND BROTHER, KOROPPI

The thing I like most about Keroppi is: ....

If I ever met Keroppi I would...

Give him a huge hug ⬭
Go swimming in Donut pond with him ⬭
Ask him to sing my favourite song ⬭

HOW TO DRAW KEROPPI

1. DRAW TWO BIG CIRCLES FOR KEROPPI'S EYES, MAKING SURE THE LEFT EYE OVERLAPS THE RIGHT ONE. ADD TWO PUPILS IN THE CENTRE OF EACH CIRCLE.

2. DRAW A HALF OVAL SHAPE UNDERNEATH THE CIRCLES FOR KEROPPI'S FACE AND ADD TWO SMALL CIRCLES FOR HIS CHEEKS AND A V-SHAPE LINE FOR HIS MOUTH.

3. NEXT DRAW HIS BODY SHAPE AND ADD IN HIS ARMS AND LEGS.

4. TO FINISH, COLOUR HIM IN. DON'T FORGET HIS BOW TIE!

19

Keroppi's Doodle Time

Get ready for some doodle fun.

Check out the funny faces Keroppi is pulling. Can you doodle some eyes and different mouth shapes on the faces below, so Keroppi looks...

happy

shocked argggggghhhhhhH!

sad

sleepy zzzzzzz

Turn these squiggles into some creatures living in Donut Pond.

What do you think Keroppi is daydreaming about?
Doodle in the dream bubble below.

Doodle a dotted line to show Keroppi's leap from his lily pad to the leaf.

Talent Spotting

Everyone has a talent... what's yours?

My main talent is:..
....
....
....
....

But I can also:

1. ....
....

2. ....
....

3. ....
....

The talents I am still working on are:

1. ....

2. ....

3. ....

My silliest secret talent that nobody knows about is

....

....

....

My most talented friends are:

1. ....

2. ....

3. ....

The talent I would most love to have is...

....

....

Too Cool for School!

Whether you love it or hate it, school is a great place for learning and trying new things and the best bit is you get to be with your besties all day long.

NAME OF YOUR SCHOOL: ....

FAVE SUBJECT: ....

WORST SUBJECT: ....

BEST TEACHER: ....

WORST TEACHER: ....

MOST AMAZING THING YOU HAVE LEARNT THIS YEAR: ....

....

DESCRIBE YOUR UNIFORM: ....

HOW DO YOU GET TO SCHOOL?: ....

SCHOOL DINNERS OR PACKED LUNCH: ....

BEST ACADEMIC ACHIEVEMENT: ....

BEST EXTRA-CURRICULUM EVENT: ....

WHICH OF THESE CLUBS DO YOU BELONG TO AT SCHOOL?:

SPORTS TEAM	CHOIR ORCHESTRA	CHESS CLUB	COOKING CLUB	DRAMA CLUB	OTHER

IF YOU WERE A TEACHER, WHAT SUBJECT WOULD YOU TEACH AND WHY?: ....

WHAT DO YOU WANT TO BE WHEN YOU LEAVE SCHOOL?: ....

....

WHY DO YOU THINK YOU'D BE GOOD AT IT?: ....

....

24

Design the perfect school uniform.

HELP MR WHITE FINISH OFF THESE SCHOOL REPORTS FOR HIS PUPILS.

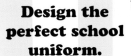

8+6=

Don't forget your school bag.

Add a cool school logo to your outfit.

STUDENT NAME: Keroppi

SUBJECT	GRADE	COMMENT
MATHS	B	....
MUSIC	....	Amazing singing - well done
....	C	Must stop throwing paper aeroplanes

STUDENT NAME: Chococat

SUBJECT	GRADE	COMMENT
MATHS	D	Has trouble counting on his paws
GEOGRAPHY	B+	....
SOCIAL SKILLS	....	Always knows what's going on thanks to his antennae

STUDENT NAME: Badtz-Maru

SUBJECT	GRADE	COMMENT
COOKERY	C-	Scoffs the ingredients before he can cook them
COMPUTERS	....	Must do better. Is addicted to playing games!
SPORT	A	....

STUDENT NAME: My Melody

SUBJECT	GRADE	COMMENT
COOKING	A	An expert at cookies and cakes
GEOGRAPHY	....	Great at finding her way through a forest
ENGLISH	C	....

Good Spot

You'll need an eagle eye to complete these puzzles.

1. WHICH TWO KEROPPI'S ARE THE SAME?

2. WHICH SHADOW BELONGS TO KEROPPI?

1

2

3

4

5

6

Answers on page 94

My Melody

Sweet and gentle My Melody is a cute little bunny who lives in the forest. Her favourite hobby is baking and she loves making delicious cookies with her mum and scoffing cake with her friend Flat the mouse.

I LOVE My Melody

Factfile

NAME: MY MELODY
BIRTHDAY: 18 JANUARY
LIVES: IN THE FOREST OF MARILANDE
LIKES: PLAYING WITH FLAT
FAVE THING: ALMOND POUND CAKE

Cute-o-meter!

DRAW AN ARROW ON THE CUTE-O-METER TO SHOW HOW CUTE YOU THINK MY MELODY IS.

Did you know?

HER MOST TREASURED ITEM IS HER BRIGHT HOOD, WHICH HER GRANDMOTHER GAVE HER

The thing I like most about My Melody is: ....

If I ever met My Melody I would...

Ask her to bake me some cookies ◯

Tell her to stand up to Kuromi ◯

Make her a cute daisy chain ◯

HOW TO DRAW MY MELODY

1. DRAW A CIRCLE FOR THE HEAD AND A SMALLER CIRCLE FOR THE BODY.

2. DRAW IN MELODY'S EARS, BOW AND A SMALLER CIRCLE TO CREATE HER HOOD.

3. ADD CIRCLES FOR HER EYES AND NOSE AND A LARGE DOT FOR HER MOUTH.

4. TO FINISH, ADD THE COLLAR OF HER CAPE, HER ARMS AND LEGS AND COLOUR HER IN.

29

My Melody's Doodle Time

Grab your pencil and get squiggling...

Doodle some new hats for My Melody here.

What do you think My Melody is daydreaming about?
Doodle in the dream bubble below.

Doodle some fish on the end of My Melody's fishing line and swimming about in the pond.

My Melody loves to relax in the sunshine. Doodle some cool sunglasses on her face.

Best Friends Forever

It takes all sorts of qualities to make the perfect friend.
Answer the questions below to show what you rate in a mate.

Who is your kindest friend?:

....

**Which friend cheers you up
when you're feeling rubbish?:**

....

WHO IS YOUR BEST BEST BEST BFF?:

....

WHO IS YOUR MOST STYLISH
FRIEND?: ....

WHO IS YOUR FUNNIEST FRIEND?:

....

WHICH FRIEND IS BEST AT KEEPING A
SECRET?: ....

WHICH FRIEND IS THE BEST DANCER?: ....
WHICH FRIEND IS THE MOST ORGANISED?: ....
WHO IS BEST TO SHOP WITH?: ....

WHICH FRIEND IS THE BEST DANCER?: ....
WHICH FRIEND IS THE MOST ORGANISED?: ....
WHO IS BEST TO SHOP WITH?: ....

**Number these qualities
1 to 5 to show what you
think is most and least
important in a friend.**

reliable ◯   lots of fun ◯

kind ◯   nice clothes ◯

can keep a secret ◯

WHICH FRIEND IS A SCATTERBRAIN?:..
WHO IS YOUR FUNNIEST FRIEND?:..
WHICH FRIEND HAVE YOU KNOWN THE LONGEST? :..
WHO IS YOUR FUNNIEST FRIEND?:..

Stick your best BFF photos here and make up some funny captions.

Take this quick quiz to find out what kind of friend you are.

1. WHEN YOU ARE WITH YOUR FRIENDS DO YOU...
A) gossip constantly
B) listen
C) do both

2. DO YOU HAVE...
A) lots of friends, old and new
B) friends you have known forever
C) one or two very close besties

3. HOW OFTEN DO YOU TEXT YOUR FRIENDS...
A) every couple of minutes
B) every couple of hours
C) every couple of days

4. WHEN YOU HEAR A SECRET DO YOU...
A) tell everyone you know
B) tell no one
C) only tell your bestie

MOSTLY AS
You are a brilliant buddy, the life and soul of the party and have loads of mates, rather than a few close ones.

MOSTLY BS
Everyone likes and trusts you and wants to be your friend. You make a lot of effort with your friendships and your pals appreciate it.

MOSTLY CS
You prefer to have only one or two really close besties, who you do everything with and would do anything for.

Maze Madness

Uh oh! My Melody and Flat are lost in the forest...
can you help them find their way home?

START

EYE SPY...

HOW MANY FLOWERS CAN YOU SPOT?

HOW MANY BUTTERFLIES CAN YOU SEE?

COUNT UP THE TOADSTOOLS ALONG THE PATHS?

Answers on page 94

Birthday Bash

Birthdays are the best. You get to be the centre of attention and have heaps of cool pressies from your family and besties.
Make sure you're all set for your next birthday with this party prep list!

PRESENT WISH LIST - I WANT:

1. ....
2. ....
3. ....
4. ....
5. ....

TOP 5 PARTY GUESTS:

1. ....
2. ....
3. ....
4. ....
5. ....

Type of party:

DISCO ☐ SLEEPOVER ☐ BOWLING ☐ CINEMA ☐ PIZZA ☐

PAINTBALLING ☐ OTHER ....

Where will you have your party?:

....

What will you wear?:

....

Dream celeb guest:

....

Make sure you remember all your family and friends' birthdays by writing them here.

Name:.........................
Birthday:.....................
Age:............................
Star sign:....................
Perfect present: ....

Name:.........................
Birthday:.....................
Age:............................
Star sign:....................
Perfect present: ....

Name:.........................
Birthday:.....................
Age:............................
Star sign:....................
Perfect present: ....

Name:.........................
Birthday:.....................
Age:............................
Star sign:....................
Perfect present: ....

Name:.........................
Birthday:.....................
Age:............................
Star sign:....................
Perfect present: ....

Name:.........................
Birthday:.....................
Age:............................
Star sign:....................
Perfect present: ....

What star sign are you and do you know all about your ruling planet and birthstone? Read on to find out more...

AQUARIUS -
21 JAN TO 19 FEB
ELEMENT: air
RULING PLANET: Uranus
SYMBOL: water bearer
STONE: garnet and amethyst
CHARACTERISTICS:
Aquarians are big thinkers and friendly but don't like to talk about their feelings too much

PISCES -
20 FEB TO 20 MAR
ELEMENT: water
RULING PLANET: Neptune
SYMBOL: the fish
STONE: amethyst and aquamarine
CHARACTERISTICS: like other water signs, you are sensitive of your own feelings and those of others

ARIES -
21 MAR TO 20 APR
ELEMENT: fire
RULING PLANET: Mars
SYMBOL: the ram
STONE: aquamarine and diamond
CHARACTERISTICS: you are adventurous, outgoing and active

TAURUS -
21 APR TO 21 MAY
ELEMENT: earth
RULING PLANET: Venus
SYMBOL: the bull
STONE: diamond and emerald
CHARACTERISTICS: you don't like change and can be quite stubborn but have the determination to always get what you want

GEMINI -
22 MAY TO 21 JUNE
ELEMENT: air
RULING PLANET: Mercury
SYMBOL: twins
STONE: emerald and pearl
CHARACTERISTICS: you are funny and chatty and have lots of friends but can be a perfectionist

CANCER -
22 JUNE TO 23 JULY
ELEMENT: water
RULING PLANET: the moon
SYMBOL: the crab
STONE: pearl and ruby
CHARACTERISTICS: you can be quite moody but are always loyal and protective of your friends

LEO -
24 JULY TO 23 AUG
ELEMENT: fire
RULING PLANET: the Sun
SYMBOL: the lion
STONE: ruby and peridot
CHARACTERISTICS: you are generous and warm-hearted but can be a bit bossy at times

VIRGO -
24 AUG TO 23 SEP
ELEMENT: earth
RULING PLANET: Mercury
SYMBOL: girl
STONE: peridot and sapphire
CHARACTERISTICS: modest and shy, you sometimes think too much and can be a bit of a worrier

LIBRA -
24 SEP TO 23 OCT
ELEMENT: air
RULING PLANET: Venus
SYMBOL: weighing scales
STONE: sapphire and opal
DESCRIPTION: you are always fair and easy going but can sometimes be too easily influenced by others

SCORPIO -
24 OCT TO 22 NOV
ELEMENT: water
RULING PLANET: Pluto
SYMBOL: the scorpion
STONE: opal and citrine
CHARACTERISTICS: determined and emotional, sometimes you get jealous and obsess over little things

SAGITTARIUS -
23 NOV TO 21 DEC
ELEMENT: fire
RULING PLANET: Jupiter
SYMBOL: the archer
STONE: citrine and topaz
CHARACTERISTICS: You are always honest and straight forward but can sometimes be careless

CAPRICORN -
22 DEC TO 20 JAN
ELEMENT: earth
RULING PLANET: Saturn
SYMBOL: the goat
STONE: topaz and garnet
CHARACTERISTICS: practical and careful, you can sometimes be a bit pessimistic about life

Kuromi

Wild and boisterous, Kuromi loves to make trouble and mischief wherever she goes. Despite her tough and rebellious image, deep down Kuromi is quite sweet. She won't admit it but she loves reading romance novels and writing in her diary.

I LOVE Kuromi

Factfile

NAME: KUROMI
BIRTHDAY: 31 OCTOBER (HALLOWEEN)
LIKES: BEING MEAN AND MOODY
FAVE COLOUR: BLACK
FAVE THING: ONIONS

Cute-o-meter!

cute

really cute

super cute

DRAW AN ARROW ON THE CUTE-O-METER TO SHOW HOW CUTE YOU THINK KUROMI IS.

KUROMI IS MY MELODY'S RIVAL AND LEADER OF THE BIKER GANG KUROMI 5

The thing I like most about Kitty is: ....

If I ever met Kuromi I would…

Tell her to be nicer to My Melody ◯   Borrow her cool skull hat ◯   Ask to hang out with Kuromi 5 ◯

HOW TO DRAW KUROMI

1. DRAW A BIG CIRCLE FOR KUROMI'S HEAD AND ADD TWO LINES TO THE TOP. THEN DRAW HER BODY WITH AN ARM AND TAIL LINE.

2. DRAW IN HER ARROW-SHAPED EARS, WITH A SMALL CIRCLE ON THE TOP OF EACH ONE AND THE OUTLINE OF HER HOOD ACROSS HER FACE.

3. DRAW IN KUROMI'S EYES, NOSE AND MOUTH AND ADD THE SKULL TO HER HOOD AND A COLLAR AROUND HER NECK.

4. TO FINISH, ADD HER ARMS, LEGS AND TAIL AND COLOUR HER IN.

Kuromi's Doodle Time

Get ready for squillions of squiggles…

Fancy yourself as a fashion designer?
Doodle some new hat designs for Kuromi.

Doodle some hearts here.

Use these ones for some inspiration.

What do you think Kuromi is daydreaming about?
Doodle in the dream bubble below.

Finish off these cool party decorations for Kuromi's Halloween birthday.

Daydreamer

Everyone has a dream – whether it's a dream holiday, a dream job
or a dream you have when you're fast asleep.
Use the space below to write all about the dreams you have.

DREAM JOB: ....

DREAM HOLIDAY: ....

DREAM OUTFIT: ....

DREAM DAY: ....

DREAM BOY: ....

What would your dream home be like?:

A CASTLE 🤍   A PENTHOUSE 🤍   APARTMENT 🤍

A MANSION 🤍   A COTTAGE 🤍   A CAMPERVAN 🤍

Which would you rather be for one day?:

INVISIBLE ⬤   FATHER CHRISTMAS ⬤

A MILLIONAIRE ⬤   A POPSTAR ⬤

A PRINCESS ⬤

Dream Decoder

Falling dreams

IF YOU DREAM YOU ARE FALLING, EITHER FROM THE SKY OR DOWN A CLIFF EDGE OR
HOLE, THIS CAN MEAN YOU FEEL OUT OF CONTROL. TRY TO WORK OUT
WHAT AREA OF YOUR LIFE YOU NEED TO TAKE CONTROL OF AND
WHAT YOU CAN DO AND THESE DREAMS WILL STOP.

Being naked dreams

DREAMING YOU HAVE FORGOTTEN TO PUT YOUR CLOTHES ON USUALLY MEANS YOU
ARE FEELING INSECURE OR WORRIED ABOUT SOMETHING. IT CAN ALSO MEAN YOU
ARE TRYING TO HIDE YOUR TRUE SELF. TRY TO STOP WORRYING AND BE TRUE TO
YOURSELF AND YOU'LL SOON STOP HAVING THIS DREAM.

Flying dreams

DREAMING OF FLYING MEANS YOU ARE FEELING CONFIDENT AND SECURE ABOUT
YOUR LIFE AND TOTALLY IN CONTROL. IF YOU WORRY THAT YOU ARE FLYING TOO
HIGH IN YOUR DREAM, IT SOMETIMES MEANS YOU ARE WORRIED ABOUT HOW YOUR
SUCCESS WILL CHANGE YOU AND YOUR LIFE.

DATE: ....

WHAT HAPPENS IN THE DREAM?:
....
....

HOW DID IT MAKE YOU FEEL?:
....

WHAT DID IT MEAN?: ....
....

DATE: ....

WHAT HAPPENS IN THE DREAM?:
....
....

HOW DID IT MAKE YOU FEEL?:
....

WHAT DID IT MEAN?: ....
....

DATE: ....

WHAT HAPPENS IN THE DREAM?:
....
....

HOW DID IT MAKE YOU FEEL?:
....

WHAT DID IT MEAN?: ....
....

DATE: ....

WHAT HAPPENS IN THE DREAM?:
....
....

HOW DID IT MAKE YOU FEEL?:
....

WHAT DID IT MEAN?: ....
....

Secret Code Cracker

Use the secret code card below to crack the code and work out what these characters are planning to get up to on the weekend.

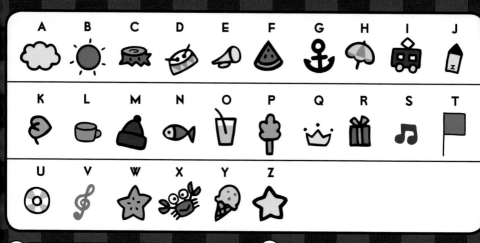

1 Keroppi says:

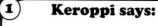

2 Hello Kitty says:

3 Chococat says:

4 Kuromi says:

If I was a...

Ever wondered what it would be like to be something completely different in life? What would you be?

If I was an animal I would be a

....

If I was a fish I would be a

....

If I was a colour I would be

....

If I was a number I would be

....

1   8   15

If I was a chocolate bar I would be

....

22   4

100

If I was a pop star I would be

....

If I was a film star I would be

....

If I was a planet I would be

....

If I was an ice-cream flavour I would be

....

If I was a flower I would be ....

If I could be anyone in the world I would be

....

If I could have a new name it would be

....

I would be the
coolest
rock star ever!

chococat

Super-cute Chococat is a brave little cat who loves fooling around and a-mew-sing his friends. He can be a bit forgetful at times but is often the first to know all the juicy gossip and what's going on, thanks to his ultra-sensitive antenna whiskers.

I LOVE chococat

Factfile

NAME: CHOCOCAT
BIRTHDAY: 10 MAY
LIVES: CHOCO-CHOCO HOUSE
LIKES: TRYING OUT DIFFERENT-COLOURED COLLARS
FAVE THING: HANGING OUT WITH HIS MATES - COOKIE BAU AND NUTZ

Cute-o-meter!

cute
really cute
super cute

DRAW AN ARROW ON THE CUTE-O-METER TO SHOW HOW CUTE YOU THINK CHOCOCAT IS.

Did you know?
CHOCOCAT WAS NAMED AFTER HIS CHOCOLATE-COLOURED NOSE

The thing I like most about Chococat is: ....

If I ever met Chococat I would...

Give him a cuddle ◯   Take a tour of Choco-Choco house ◯   Go on an adventure with him ◯

HOW TO DRAW CHOCOCAT

1. DRAW A LARGE CIRCLE WITH TWO EARS FOR CHOCOCAT'S HEAD. ADD A SMALLER (HALF) CIRCLE FOR HIS BODY BELOW.

2. NEXT, ADD HIS ARMS, LEGS AND TAIL. ARTWORK: ILLUSTRATION OF CHOCOCAT'S BODY.

3. ADD TWO LARGE CIRCLES FOR CHOCOCAT'S EYES WITH PUPILS IN, ONE SMALLER CIRCLE FOR HIS NOSE AND TWO LINES EITHER SIDE OF HIS HEAD FOR HIS WHISKERS.

4. TO FINISH, ADD HIS COLLAR AND COLOUR HIM IN.

49

Chococat's Doodle Time

Love to doodle? Draw your best ones here...

What do you think this cool cat is daydreaming about? Doodle in the dream bubble below.

Add some wheels to Chococat's bike.

Finish off these pics of Chococat so he is a complete cat – you'll need to doodle any missing whiskers, ears, eyes, tail...

Use the grid to draw the other half of Chococat's friend, Jellybean.

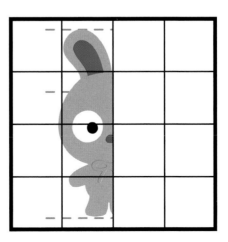

51

Perfect pastimes

What do you love to do more than anything else?
Describe your fave hobbies and activities here.

FAVE THING TO DO AFTER SCHOOL: ....

FAVE ACTIVITY ON THE WEEKEND: ....

I love to:

READ

LISTEN TO MUSIC

CHAT TO MY MATES

PLAY TENNIS

GO HORSE-RIDING

MAKE THINGS

GO TO DANCE CLASS

SING

CHILL OUT

OTHER
....

WHAT HOBBY WOULD YOU LOVE TO TAKE UP:

....

....

WHAT DO YOU WISH YOU WERE AN EXPERT AT:

....

....

Amazing experience I would love to try:

SKY-DIVING

BUNGEE JUMPING

FLYING

DEEP-SEA DIVING

HORSE RIDING

SPACE TRAVEL

OTHER
....

Fill in your weekly diary here – which day is your favourite?

MONDAY ....

TUESDAY ....

WEDNESDAY ....

THURSDAY...

FRIDAY...

SATURDAY...

SUNDAY..

FAVE DAY: ....

Chococat

MONDAY -	NOTHING - BORING!!
TUESDAY -	CYCLE TO THE PARK
WEDNESDAY -	MEET UP WITH CHARMMY KITTY TO CHASE MICE
THURSDAY -	MY MELODY COMING TO TEA AT CHOCO-CHOCO HOUSE
FRIDAY -	GO ROLLER-SKATING WITH COOKIE BAU AND NUTZ
SATURDAY -	GET A NEW COLLAR
SUNDAY -	DON'T FORGET KEROPPI'S BIRTHDAY PARTY- BUY HIM A NEW BOW TIE

Fab Fashion

Chococat

FAVE ITEMS IN YOUR WARDROBE:

Got a passion for fashion? Describe your style and fashion faves here…

1. ....
2. ....
3. ....
4. ....
5. ....

FASHION WISH-LIST – I WANT…

1. ....
2. ....
3. ....
4. ....
5. ....

FAVE CELEBRITY STYLE: ....

BEST ACCESSORY: ....

FAVE SHOES: ....

MOST PRECIOUS PIECE OF JEWELLERY: ....

FAVE FRIEND'S STYLE: ....

You look good in:

green

 **brown**

 pink

 red

 **black**

blue

yellow

orange

Work out which colours look great together by using this Colour fashion wheel.

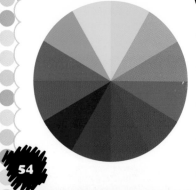

- COLOURS THAT ARE NEXT TO EACH OTHER, LIKE YELLOW AND YELLOW-ORANGE
- COLOURS THAT FORM AN X, LIKE, ORANGE, VIOLET-RED AND YELLOW
- COLOURS THAT FORM A T, LIKE, ORANGE AND VIOLET-RED
- COLOURS AT RIGHT ANGLES WITH EACH OTHER, LIKE YELLOW AND RED-ORANGE
- COLOURS OPPOSITE EACH OTHER LIKE YELLOW AND VIOLET

White, black, brown and shades are denim are neutral and will go with anything.

What's your style?

TAKE THIS QUICK QUIZ TO FIND YOUR PERFECT LOOK.

	YES	NO
1. YOU ALWAYS PUT STYLE OVER COMFORT WHEN CHOOSING YOUR CLOTHES.	YES	NO
2. YOU FOLLOW FASHIONS AND LIKE TO BUY CLOTHES THAT EVERYONE ELSE IS WEARING.	YES	NO
3. YOU LOVE TRYING OUT NEW TRENDS AS WELL AS OLD VINTAGE AND RETRO CLOTHING.	YES	NO
4. YOU ALWAYS PLAN YOUR OUTFIT BEFORE YOU WEAR IT.	YES	NO
5. YOU HAVE LOTS OF SHOES AND ACCESSORIES.	YES	NO

Mostly YES

You love to try out new trends and keep up with the latest fashions. Try mixing a trendy skater dress, with a vintage denim jacket and cute handbag.

Mostly NO

You like to stick to favourite fashion items and wear casual clothes that you feel comfy in. Opt for a denim skirt or jeans and team with your fave t-shirt and a hand-made necklace or bracelet.

55

Quiz Time

Test your Sanrio skills and knowledge with this quiz.

Warm up round...

1. WHICH GOTHIC BUNNY WAS BORN ON HALLOWEEN?..............................
2. WHO LIVES IN DONUT POND?..
3. WHO HAS A FRIEND CALLED FLAT?...
4. WHO HAS A TWIN SISTER CALLED MIMI?...
5. WHO'S NAME ALSO MEANS X AND O...

True/False...

1. KEROPPI'S IS A TRIPLET.	T	F
2. CHARMMY KITTY WEARS A BELL AROUND HER NECK.	T	F
3. CHOCOCAT'S NOSE IS BRIGHT RED.	T	F
4. KITTY'S SURNAME IS WHITE.	T	F
5. MY MELODY LIVES IN MARILAND FOREST.	T	F

Multiple Choice...

1. BADTZ-MARU'S BIRTHDAY IS ON ...

A) CHRISTMAS DAY

B) APRIL FOOL'S DAY

C) NEW YEAR'S DAY

2. KUROMI'S GANG IS CALLED...

A) KUROMI 10

B) KUROMI COOL

C) KUROMI

3. CHOCOCAT LIVES IN...
A) CHOCO-CHOCO HOUSE
B) CHOCOLAND
C) CHOCO-LAKE

4. MY MELODY'S FAVE CAKE IS...
A) FRUIT CAKE
B) CHOCOLATE CAKE
C) ALMOND POUND CAKE

5. KEROPPI'S MUM IS A ...
A) CHEF
B) RACING CAR DRIVER
C) TEACHER

How did you do? Score: /15

1 to 5 points:
HMMM ... NOT A BAD START BUT HAVE ANOTHER GO AND SEE IF YOU CAN SCORE HIGHER.

5 to 10 points:
WELL DONE! YOU KNOW YOUR SANRIO STUFF, BUT THERE'S DEFINITELY ROOM FOR IMPROVEMENT.

Over 10 points:
WOW!!! YOUR BRAIN MUST BE BURSTING WITH FACTS AND STATS ABOUT KITTY AND HER PALS. TOP SCORE FOR YOU!

Now test your friend's and see many points they can score.

My friend's score: /15

Answers on page 94

Charmmykitty

Charmmy Kitty is a cute Persian cat, given as a present to Kitty by her Papa. Quiet and well mannered, Charmmy is the purrrrfect pet and always does as she's told. She loves to follow Kitty around and hang out with her furry friend, Sugar the hamster.

I LOVE Charmmykitty

Factfile

NAME: CHARMMY KITTY
BIRTHDAY: 31 OCTOBER
LIVES: WITH KITTY AND HER FAMILY
LIKES: BRIGHT AND SPARKLY OBJECTS
FAVE THING: KITTY

Cute-o-meter!

cute — **really cute** — **super cute**

DRAW AN ARROW ON THE CUTE-O-METER TO SHOW HOW CUTE YOU THINK CHARMMYKITTY IS.

Did you know?

CHARMMY CARRIES THE KEY TO KITTY'S JEWELLERY BOX AROUND HER NECK NECKGRANDMOTHER GAVE HER

The thing I like most about My Melody is: ....

If I ever met Charmmy Kitty I would…

Give her some bright and sparkly jewellery ○

Scratch her tummy ○

Try on her cute lace-trimmed bow ○

HOW TO DRAW CHARMMY KITTY

1. START WITH AN EGG SHAPE FOR THE HEAD AND ADD A BODY, WHICH SHOULD BE A BIT LIKE A MUSHROOM STEM.

2. DRAW IN HER FURRY CHEEKS, EARS AND BOW.

3. ADD TWO SMALL CIRCLES FOR EYES, A CUTE BUTTON NOSE AND THREE WHISKERS ON EITHER SIDE OF CHARMMY KITTY'S FACE.

4. DRAW IN HER FLUFFY TAIL, ADD A FLUFFY OUTLINE TO HER BODY AND DRAW IN HER LEGS. TO FINISH, COLOUR IN HER BOW.

Charmmy Kitty's Doodle Time

Doodle some cute kitty drawings here...

What do you think Charmmy Kitty is daydreaming about? Doodle in the dream bubble below.

Turn these squiggles into some cute hearts and flowers.

Doodle Charmmy Kitty some new bling jewellery to go with her key necklace.

Doodle some toppings on this ice cream and cupcake and finish off Charmmy Kitty's lollipop.

Word Wonders!

Bend your brain with these wordy puzzles.

1. Unscramble the letters to reveal the names of Kitty's pals.

A) ARMY TICK MYTH

_ _ _ _ _   _ _ _ _   _ _ _ _ _

B) COACH COT

_ _ _ _ _ _   _ _ _ _

C) PORK PIE

_ _ _ _ _ _ _

2. Cross out all the letters that appear twice to reveal one of Kitty's favourite things.

M J L F T R C N S Q W

P B Z A Y X H M J L F T

R N S K Q W P B Z Y E X H

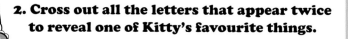

_____

3. Can you help Chococat solve these riddles?

A) IF I DON'T SHARE IT, I HAVE IT. IF I SHARE IT, I DON'T HAVE IT. WHAT IS IT?

B) WHAT GOES UP WHEN THE RAIN COMES DOWN?

C) WHAT TRAVELS AROUND BUT STAYS IN ONE SPOT?

D) WHAT HAS HANDS BUT CANNOT CLAP?

Answers on page 94

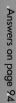

4. How many words can you make from the words below.

Kitty and friends

Here are some suggestions to start you off...

1.   IT
2.   TRY
3.   END
4.   ....
5.   ....
6.   ....
7.   ....
8.   ....
9.   ....
10.   ....
11.   ....
12.   ....
13.   ....
14.   ....
15.   ....

5 or more –
well done

10 or more –
dead impressive

15 or more –
brilliant – what a superstar!

Looking Good

If you look good, you'll feel good.
Write down your best beauty secrets here…

What beauty items do you use?

MOISTURISER   PERFUME

BODY CREAM   SHAMPOO

BODY SPRAY   CONDITIONER

HAIR DRYER   MAKE-UP

    NAIL POLISH

I brush my fur three times a day.

HOW OFTEN DO YOU...	EVERY DAY	TWICE A DAY	ONCE A WEEK	TWICE A WEEK	ONCE A MONTH	NEVER	OTHER
WASH YOUR HAIR?							
BRUSH YOUR TEETH?							
BRUSH YOUR HAIR?							
GET A HAIRCUT?							
FILE YOUR NAILS?							

Try out these beauty tips and tricks!

1. PUT SLICES OF CUCUMBER ON YOUR EYES TO FRESHEN THEM UP.
2. DRINK LOTS OF WATER EVERY DAY FOR GLOWING SKIN.
3. PUT TOOTHPASTE ON YOUR SPOTS TO GET RID OF THEM.
4. PUT TALC ON YOUR HAIR TO STOP IT LOOKING GREASY.
5. KEEP YOUR LIP-GLOSS AND NAIL POLISH IN THE FRIDGE.
6. PUT LEMON JUICE ON YOUR HAIR TO MAKE IT LIGHTER.
7. SOAK YOUR FINGERS IN OLIVE OIL TO SOFTEN YOUR CUTICLES.
8. COMB MAYONNAISE THROUGH WET HAIR FOR GLOSSY LOCKS -

DON'T FORGET TO WASH IT OUT THOUGH.

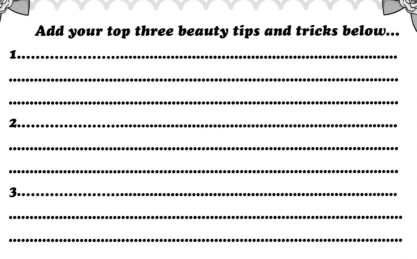

Add your top three beauty tips and tricks below...

1...
....
....
2...
....
....
3...
....
....

Brain Buster

How well do you know the Sanrio gang?
Solve the clues to reveal the characters and complete the crossword?

Across

2. This mischievous little rabbit loves making trouble and likes to rebel by wearing a skull motif on her headscarf. (6 letters)
3. A tap-dancing duck who's name begins with P. (6 letters)
6. An adorable puppy who always wears a beret. (5 letters)
8. This panda was born in China and can't stop munching apples. (9 letters)
12. The most popular frog in Donut Pond. (7 letters)
14. A feline friend named after his chocolate-covered nose. (8 letters)

15. This cute horse is a mascot for Japanese horse racing. (5 letters)
16. A cute doggy who is spot on with her fashion. (7 and 6 letters)
17. Born in the clouds, this magical puppy likes hanging out at the cafe. (11 letters)
18. A sporty panda with a heart-shaped nose. (2 and 4 letters)

Down

1. Born in Antarctica, this friendly penguin always looks smart in his bow tie. (9 letters)
4. This cute pet uses her jewel eyes to cast magical spells. (8 letters)
5. A pink rabbit who loves to wear a pretty ribbon around her ears. (12 letters)
6. This fun little pig loves surprises. (5 letters)
7. The cutest little rabbit from Mariland forest. (2 and 6 letters)
9. A sweet and friendly rabbit who loves to wish. (4, 2 and 4 letters)
10. A popular character with a greeting in her name. (5 letters)
11. Spiky and ambitious, this penguin loves to be bad. (5 and 4 letters)
13. A super-sporty pup. (8 letters)

Rearrange the letters in the purple squares to spell out the name of Hello Kitty's Persian pal.

___ ___ ___ ___ ___ ___ ___ ___ ___ ___ ___

___ ___ ___ ___ ___ ___ ___ ___

Sleepover Party

Staying up all night, stuffing your face with sweet treats and swapping secrets with your besties... what could be better!
Read on to make sure your next sleepover is party perfect!

INVITE LIST

1. ....
2. ....
3. ....
4. ....
5. ....

WHAT YOU NEED....

1. SNACKS
2. GREAT FILMS AND MUSIC
3. NEW MAKE-UP AND HAIRSTYLES TO TRY
4. COOL PYJAMAS
5. SLEEPING BAG, PILLOW AND A TORCH

SNACKS SHOPPING LIST

1. ....
2. ....
3. ....
4. ....
5. ....

FILMS WISH LIST

1. ....
2. ....
3. ....
4. ....
5. ....

TOP TUNES TO LISTEN TO

1. ....
2. ....
3. ....
4. ....
5. ....

Shimmery paws look sparkle-tastic.

Make your guests feel truly pampered by offering them a manicure or pedicure. Create some cool designs here, ready to try out on your mates.

Belt out your fave tunes on a karaoke machine. Take it in turns to perform and be judges, giving your friend with the top score a prize.

Try out some of these comments when you're on the judging panel.

KARAOKE PLAYLIST
1. ....
2. ....
3. ....
4. ....
5. ....

'NOT YOUR GREATEST PERFORMANCE, THAT SONG WAS WRONG FOR YOU.'

'IF YOU ARE THINKING OF GOING INTO THE MUSIC BIZ – DON'T!'

'YOU MADE THAT SONG YOUR OWN.'

'THAT WAS THE BEST PERFORMANCE OF THE NIGHT.'

If it's hot outside, transform your sleepover into a camping trip. Pitch a tent in your garden and decorate some trees with fairy lights. Don't forget to check with your parents that it's ok to sleep outside and keep an eye out for creepy crawlies...

Have loads of great games to play, like Truth Or Dare, where you take it in turns to either answer a question truthfully or take a dare, or Truth & Lies, where you take it in turns to tell two true things and one lie about yourself and your friends have got to guess which is the lie.

69

Badtz★Maru

Ambitious Badtz-Maru dreams of being the boss of everything and will happily admit he doesn't like anything except himself! This spiky little penguin loves to be bad and getting up to mischief with his friends, a giant panda called Pandaba and Hana Maru, a white seal.

I LOVE Badtz-Maru

Factfile

NAME:	BADTZ-MARU
BIRTHDAY:	1 APRIL (APRIL FOOLS' DAY)
LIVES:	GORGEOUS TOWN
LIKES:	COLLECTING PICTURES OF MOVIE STARS WHO PLAY BAD GUYS
FAVE THING:	ADVENTURE SPORTS AND HIMSELF

X O

DRAW AN ARROW ON THE CUTE-O-METER TO SHOW HOW CUTE YOU THINK BADTZ-MARU IS.

Did you know?

HIS NAME BADTZ, MEANS A CROSS OR X AND MARU MEANS A CIRCLE OR O. IN JAPAN THESE ARE SYMBOLS FOR RIGHT AND WRONG

The thing I like most about Badtz-Maru is: ....

If I ever met Badtz-Maru I would…

Tell him how cool he is ◯	Take him out for some sushi ◯	Ask to meet his pet alligator, Pochii ◯

HOW TO DRAW BADTZ-MARU

1. DRAW AN OVAL FOR BADTZ-MARU'S HEAD, WITH FOUR SPIKES FOR HIS HAIR AND A ROUNDED-EDGED SQUARE FOR HIS BODY.

2. ADD IN TWO HALF CIRCLES FOR HIS EYES, HIS BLACK PUPILS AND HIS BEAK.

3. ADD IN HIS LITTLE WINGS AND FLAT FEET.

4. DRAW IN HIS TUMMY AND COLOUR HIM IN.

71

Badtz-Maru's Doodle Time

Grab your pencils and get scribbling and squiggling…

Doodle some backgrounds to these Badtz-Maru action shots!

Secret agent XO…(license to thrill!!)

'Wooooooo-hoooooo!' Surf's up dudes!

What do you think Badtz-Maru is daydreaming about?
Doodle in the dream bubble below.

Give Badtz-Maru some even crazier hairstyles.

Finish off this doodle of a treasure island for Pirate Badtz-Maru.

Badtz-Maru Sudoku!

Test how clever you are with this brain-bending Sudoku puzzle.

Each column, row and 4 x 4 square should have all four different Badtz-Maru Poses.

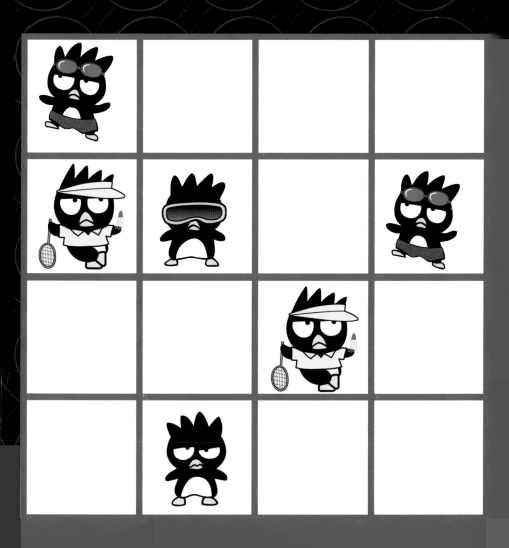

Holiday Fun

Holidays are the best. Whether you're at home or abroad they are loads of fun and create special memories that will last forever.

BEST HOLIDAY MEMORY: ....

WORST HOLIDAY MEMORY:..

FAVE PERSON TO GO ON HOLIDAY WITH:.................................

THE CELEBRITY I'D MOST LIKE TO GO ON HOLIDAY WITH IS:

....

I CAN'T GO ON HOLIDAY WITHOUT MY:....................................

My fave kind of holiday is a:

CAMPING HOLIDAY

BEACH HOLIDAY

SAFARI HOLIDAY

ACTIVITY HOLIDAY

CITY SIGHTSEEING HOLIDAY

Stick your best holiday snaps here.

Top tourist spots I want to visit:	Music I like to listen to chilling on the beach:	Books I like to read, lying by the pool:
1	1	1 ....
2	2	2 ....
3	3	3 ....
4	4	4 ....
5	5	5 ....

Dear..........................
Having the most AMAZING time
skiing in..........................
I entered a ski competition and
came.............and won a ......
....
I was really awesome/rubbish/lucky!
Laters,

XO (aka the **best** skier in the
world! Ever!)

Music Madness

Do you love to sing along to your fave tunes? Can't help bustin' some moves when you hear the beat? Write about your perfect popstars and playlists here...

FAVE SINGER: ....

FAVE BAND: ....

BEST SONG EVER: ....

....

BEST SONG IN THE CHARTS NOW:

....

....

BEST MUSIC VIDEO EVER: ....

....

BEST MUSIC VIDEO IN THE
CHARTS NOW: ....

....

BEST SONG TO DANCE TO: ....

....

BEST SONG TO SING IN THE
SHOWER: ....

....

BEST LINE IN A SONG: ....

....

....

....

INVITE LIST

1. ....

2. ....

3. ....

4. ....

5. ....

FIVE SONGS YOU KNOW ALL THE WORDS TO:

1. ....

2. ....

3. ....

4. ....

5. ....

CAN YOU PLAY A MUSICAL INSTRUMENT?: ....

IF YOU COULD PLAY ANY INSTRUMENT WHAT WOULD IT BE?: ....

....

IF YOU HAD A BAND, WHAT WOULD YOU CALL IT?: ....

WHAT KIND OF MUSIC WOULD YOUR BAND PLAY?: ....

WHAT KIND OF LOOK WOULD YOUR BAND HAVE?: ....

....

MAKE UP YOUR OWN SONG AND WRITE THE LYRICS HERE.

IF YOU'RE STUCK FOR INSPIRATION, PICK AN IMPORTANT EVENT IN

YOUR LIFE OR A HAPPY OR SAD MEMORY TO GET YOUR STARTED.

VERSE

....

....

....

....

....

CHORUS

....

....

....

....

JANUARY PLANNER

Make sure you don't miss a party, school deadline or outing with your besties with this great planner...

1 ....
2 ....
3 ....
4 ....
5 ....
6 ....
7 ....
8 ....
9 ....
10 ....
11 ....
12 ....
13 ....
14 ....
15 ....
16 ....
17 ....
18 ....
19 ....
20 ....
21 ....
22 ....
23 ....
24 ....
25 ....
26 ....
27 ....
28 ....
29 ....
30 ....
31 ....

FEBRUARY PLANNER

1 ....
2 ....
3 ....
4 ....
5 ....
6 ....
7 ....
8 ....
9 ....
10 ....
11 ....
12 ....
13 ....
14 ....
15 ....
16 ....
17 ....
18 ....
19 ....
20 ....
21 ....
22 ....
23 ....
24 ....
25 ....
26 ....
27 ....
28 ....
29 ....

MARCH PLANNER

1 ....
2 ....
3 ....
4 ....
5 ....
6 ....
7 ....
8 ....
9 ....
10 ....
11 ....
12 ....
13 ....
14 ....
15 ....
16 ....
17 ....
18 ....
19 ....
20 ....
21 ....
22 ....
23 ....
24 ....
25 ....
26 ....
27 ....
28 ....
29 ....
30 ....
31 ....

APRIL PLANNER

1 ....
2 ....
3 ....
4 ....
5 ....
6 ....
7 ....
8 ....
9 ....
10 ....
11 ....
12 ....
13 ....
14 ....
15 ....
16 ....
17 ....
18 ....
19 ....
20 ....
21 ....
22 ....
23 ....
24 ....
25 ....
26 ....
27 ....
28 ....
29 ....
30 ....

MAY PLANNER

1 ....
2 ....
3 ....
4 ....
5 ....
6 ....
7 ....
8 ....
9 ....
10 ....
11 ....
12 ....
13 ....
14 ....
15 ....
16 ....
17 ....
18 ....
19 ....
20 ....
21 ....
22 ....
23 ....
24 ....
25 ....
26 ....
27 ....
28 ....
29 ....
30 ....
31 ....

JUNE PLANNER

1 ....
2 ....
3 ....
4 ....
5 ....
6 ....
7 ....
8 ....
9 ....
10 ....
11 ....
12 ....
13 ....
14 ....
15 ....
16 ....
17 ....
18 ....
19 ....
20 ....
21 ....
22 ....
23 ....
24 ....
25 ....
26 ....
27 ....
28 ....
29 ....
30 ....

JULY PLANNER

1 ....
2 ....
3 ....
4 ....
5 ....
6 ....
7 ....
8 ....
9 ....
10 ....
11 ....
12 ....
13 ....
14 ....
15 ....
16 ....
17 ....
18 ....
19 ....
20 ....
21 ....
22 ....
23 ....
24 ....
25 ....
26 ....
27 ....
28 ....
29 ....
30 ....
31 ....

AUGUST PLANNER

1 ....
2 ....
3 ....
4 ....
5 ....
6 ....
7 ....
8 ....
9 ....
10 ....
11 ....
12 ....
13 ....
14 ....
15 ....
16 ....
17 ....
18 ....
19 ....
20 ....
21 ....
22 ....
23 ....
24 ....
25 ....
26 ....
27 ....
28 ....
29 ....
30 ....
31 ....

SEPTEMBER PLANNER

1 ....
2 ....
3 ....
4 ....
5 ....
6 ....
7 ....
8 ....
9 ....
10 ....
11 ....
12 ....
13 ....
14 ....
15 ....
16 ....
17 ....
18 ....
19 ....
20 ....
21 ....
22 ....
23 ....
24 ....
25 ....
26 ....
27 ....
28 ....
29 ....
30 ....

OCTOBER PLANNER

1 ....
2 ....
3 ....
4 ....
5 ....
6 ....
7 ....
8 ....
9 ....
10 ....
11 ....
12 ....
13 ....
14 ....
15 ....
16 ....
17 ....
18 ....
19 ....
20 ....
21 ....
22 ....
23 ....
24 ....
25 ....
26 ....
27 ....
28 ....
29 ....
30 ....
31 ....

NOVEMBER PLANNER

1 ....
2 ....
3 ....
4 ....
5 ....
6 ....
7 ....
8 ....
9 ....
10 ....
11 ....
12 ....
13 ....
14 ....
15 ....
16 ....
17 ....
18 ....
19 ....
20 ....
21 ....
22 ....
23 ....
24 ....
25 ....
26 ....
27 ....
28 ....
29 ....
30 ....

DECEMBER PLANNER

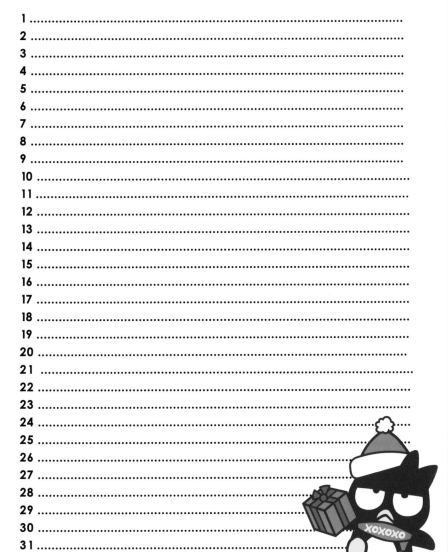

1 ....
2 ....
3 ....
4 ....
5 ....
6 ....
7 ....
8 ....
9 ....
10 ....
11 ....
12 ....
13 ....
14 ....
15 ....
16 ....
17 ....
18 ....
19 ....
20 ....
21 ....
22 ....
23 ....
24 ....
25 ....
26 ....
27 ....
28 ....
29 ....
30 ....
31 ....

Answers

P 12-13 WORDPLAY

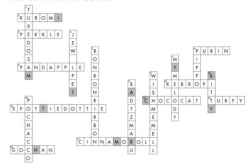

L	T	L	E	D	Y	L	M	M	N	W	C	Y	S	P
N	I	Z	E	R	H	Y	X	E	K	I	I	T	P	U
I	C	T	D	I	M	A	N	P	N	T	M	T	O	R
P	P	N	T	L	N	U	C	N	N	E	O	I	T	I
A	P	A	P	L	L	O	A	A	O	L	I	R	K	T	N
L	L	O	O	J	E	M	D	P	C	A	U	O	I	M
B	D	P	J	R	O	T	P	R	X	A	K	L	E	O
Y	R	F	P	R	E	A	W	R	A	A	X	L	D	N
T	E	M	O	O	D	K	J	I	L	E	G	E	O	K
Z	D	L	K	N	S	V	X	I	N	M	D	H	T	I
I	L	L	A	P	E	K	K	L	E	S	G	L	T	C
N	X	P	Y	J	Y	J	O	Y	G	L	T	K	I	H
T	U	X	E	D	O	S	A	M	F	G	K	A	E	I
U	R	A	M	Z	T	D	A	B	F	B	C	C	R	N
O	C	C	A	H	C	O	P	Z	Y	T	F	J	R	S

CHOCOCAT IS MISSING

P 15 CHARACTERS' FAVE THINGS

KEROPPI - SWIMMING IN DONUT POND
KITTY - BAKING COOKIES
BADTZ-MARU - EXTREME SPORTS AND
KICKING BUTT
KUROMI - GETTING UP TO NO GOOD

P20-21 GOOD SPOT

1. KEROPPI B AND H ARE THE SAME
2. SHADOW 6 IS KEROPPI

P34-35 MAZE MADNESS

PATH B LEADS TO MY MELODY'S HOUSE
15 FLOWERS, 10 BUTTERFLIES AND 8 TOAD-
STOOLS

P44-45 SECRET CODE CRACKER

1. I AM GOING SWIMMING
2. I WILL BE BAKING DELICIOUS COOKIES
3. IT'S CHILL TIME WITH MY FRIENDS
4. ANYTHING, EXCEPT HOMEWORK
5. I AM GOING FOR A WALK WITH FLAT
6. KERPOW! I WILL BE BOXING
7. MEOW... PLAYING WITH KITTY

P56-57 QUIZ TIME

WARM UP: 1. KUROMI 2. KEROPPI 3. MY MELODY
4. KITTY 5. BADTZ-MARU
TRUE OR FALSE: 1. TRUE 2. FALSE 3. FALSE
4. TRUE 5. TRUE
MULTIPLE CHOICE: 1. B 2. C 3. A 4. C 5. A

P62-63 WORD WONDERS!

1. A) CHARMMY KITTY B) CHOCOCAT C) KEROPPI
2. CAKE
3. A) SECRET B) UMBRELLA C) STAMP D) CLOCK
4. HERE ARE SOME SUGGESTIONS: TRY, IT, END,
TIE, DAD, SAD, KITE, SIT, FRIED, SAND, TATTY,
DIED, TRIED, NASTY, TRENDY, RISK, TASK ADD, FAT,
REST...

P66-67 BRAIN BUSTER

CHARMMY KITTY

P75 BADTZ-MARU SUDOKU!

94